First published 2003 by **Contender Books**
Contender Books is a division of
The Contender Entertainment Group
48 Margaret Street
London W1W 8SE
www.contendergroup.com/books

This edition published 2003

1 3 5 7 9 10 8 6 4 2

ISBN 1 84357 094 7

This is not an official Busted product nor has it been endorsed by the band or their management.

Picture Credits:

Goff Photos:	front cover, 11, 30, 31, 54, 55.
PA Photos:	6, 29, 41, 54, 55.
Rex Features:	10, 12, 13, 14, 16, 17, 19, 20, 23, 24, 25, 28, 34, 36, 42, 46, 47, 49, 50, 53, 57, 58.
All Action Pictures:	2, 3, 8, 39, 62, 63, back cover.

Text: **Lucie Cave**
Production: **Kate Gribble**
Design: **Button One to One**
Printed in the UK by **Bath Press**

BUSTED
Unofficial Annual 2004

LA
Von Dutch
DEEP
HROAT

BUSTED

CONTENTS

Introduction	9
Being Busted	10
Before Busted	15
Busted Buried... but where?	21
Busted Breakthrough	22
House Rules	26
Busted Confidential	32
Busted Crossword	35
Busted Babe Bible	37
Which Busted Babe are you?	40
Which Busted Boy are you?	43
Style Secrets	44
Busted Behaving Badly	48
Behind the Videos	50
Did you know?	52
Psychic James's Future Predictions	54
Busted Live!	56
Busted's Bigger Things To Come	59
Discography	60
Bust or Sussed?	61

Marshall

In 2002 Charlie Simpson, Matt Jay and James Bourne blasted their way into the charts with an infectious brand of guitar pop, electric energy and swoonsome smiles. Since then they've become the first band ever to enter the charts at numbers three, two and one consecutively with their first three singles, they've melted the hearts of babes across Britain and swapped numbers with celebs worldwide. In this annual you'll find out everything there is to know about the boys – from their dream date to where they get their clothes, what their bedrooms are like and their most intimate thoughts. Get stuck in!

Being Busted

BUSTED

Matt

Name	Matt Jay
Date of Birth	8 May 1983
Star sign	Taurus
Roots	Kingston
Siblings	Brother Darren and sister Amanda
Endearing feature	Ability to pull more faces than a monkey (and still look gorgeous)
Phobia	Stilton cheese – because "there's no need for mouldy food!"
Couldn't live without...	His fave CD *Make Yourself* by Incubus
Bad habit	He can burp for 26 seconds straight!
Obsessions	West Ham
Sporty?	He likes to think of himself as a skateboarder but according to James, "Matt can't do any tricks!"
Favourite phrase	His fave words are 'panini' and 'pee-pee'
Random fact	He can say the alphabet backwards
One more thing...	When he was younger he had to shave off all his hair because he'd put chewing gum behind his ear before he went to sleep – and woke with it stuck to his head!

Charlie

Name	Charlie Simpson
Date of Birth	7 June 1985
Star sign	Gemini
Roots	Ipswich
Siblings	Two older brothers Will and Ed
Endearing feature	The best and biggest eyebrows in the business (as well as a jaw so chiselled it could cut paper)
Phobia	Petrified of fish. He says, "Even the smell can make me chuck"
Couldn't live without…	His guitar
Bad habit	He stands accused of having the smelliest feet in Footville
Obsessions	The Deftones, Jimmy Eat World, Britney Spears…
Sporty?	He's a member of a gym but he doesn't use it. But he does try to go snowboarding once a year
Favourite phrase	Charlie makes the other lads chuckle with his unique posh sayings. James laughs, "He often says 'Ah the vulgarity of it all!' and puts 'idge' or 'ster' on to the end of words. He calls us 'mate-idge' – it's so random!"
Random fact	His mum calls him Farley or Farleykins
One more thing…	At 6'4" Charlie is one of the tallest men in pop – and he's still growing!

James

Name	James Bourne
Date of Birth	13 September 1983
Star sign	Virgo
Roots	Southend-on-sea
Siblings	Brothers Chris and Nick, and sister Mel
Endearing feature	A grin so big, and teeth so white, he's in danger of outshining the sun
Phobia	Horses (they freak him out) and eggs
Couldn't live without...	Jaffa Cakes
Bad habit	He picks his nose till it bleeds! Eww…
Obsessions	Blink 182, Michael Jackson, Sum 41, Britney Spears…
Sporty?	Yup. This lad is a bundle of energy and loves surfing, table tennis and shooting pool
Favourite phrase	Anything as long as it sounds like Jim Carrey (James always has the lads in stitches with his impressions)
Random fact	He has a photographic memory and knows all the words to the films he watches
One more thing…	Strange but true: he has an impressive collection of car hub caps at home

JONELLE

Before Busted

BUSTED

It might be hard to imagine a world before Busted, but believe it or not there was a time when the tastiest trio in town were just school boys dreaming of a future on planet pop. Here's the low-down on everything - from what they really went to school for, to their worst jobs, biggest hopes and earliest memories...

MEMORIES... ARE MADE OF THIS

Charlie: "I was about five and my mum was asleep on the couch. I went in and chopped her hair off! Literally chunks of it – she had to completely change her haircut!"

James: "My mum would never let me leave the table until I'd finished all my food. I used to have fits and bash my head on the floor. It's probably permanently damaged me!"

Matt: "I once accepted a dare to turn up at my best mate's school for a day and pretend I was a new kid. It was awesome! I just mucked around and caused absolute havoc all day."

WORST JOBS

Matt: "I had to cut grass around these massive open top tanks filled with human poo!"

Charlie: "My scummiest job ever was pulling wild oats in a field all day."

James: "I can't even tell you what my worst job was because it was so bad!"

BUSTED

SCHOOL REPORTS

- **James** hated learning Latin so much he tried to avoid it by hiding in a cupboard for the whole lesson. But the trick backfired because he didn't get out quick enough before the next class started - and ended up stuck in there for a whole 90 minutes! James admits: " I got seriously stressed about Latin."
- **Matt** has always been good at telling porky pies to teachers to get out of doing his homework, but he sometimes got a bit carried away with his stories. Matt laughs, "I once told a teacher 'I left my bag in a shop on the way home and now I've lost everything' – I was such a liar!"
- **Charlie** went to posh uppercrust boarding school Uppingham Public School, where his uniform consisted of a cravat and a brown jacket (the school was sooo posh it had its own nightclub!)
- **Matt's** famous face pulling started from an early age! He recalls, "I remember one time I was standing behind my teacher making all kinds of cheeky faces and stuff without realising she could see my reflection in the window!"
- **Charlie** once had his trousers pulled down in the girls' common room!
- **Matt** had a massive crush on one of his science teachers when he was 13 (this was the inspiration for Busted's first track 'What I Go To School For'). He even took her a bunch of flowers once!
- **Matt** cheekily remembers one misdemeanor in particular: "My teacher had a really nice bum. Once, before she came into the classroom, me and my mate covered her chair in flesh-coloured paint. When she sat down it stuck to her dress and gave her these bum-cheek prints. She knew it was us but she couldn't prove it!"

BUSTED

SIGNS OF STARDOM

- **Charlie** played Fat Sam in his school production of *Bugsy Malone*. He had to wear a bright orange suit and have his hair slicked back like a grease monkey, but he says "I loved being in plays - it helped get the girls!" And not only did it get him the girls, he was so good in *Bugsy* that he won a drama scholarship to Nottingham!
- When **Matt** was 14 he won a scholarship to the Sylvia Young Theatre School – he shared a class with the likes of Billie Piper and Lee Ryan from Blue.
- **Matt** had a walk-on part in *EastEnders* before he joined Busted!
- **James** was in Fagin's gang in a West End production of *Oliver!* at the London Palladium (although he'd rather we didn't know that!).

BUSTED

MUSICAL MANOEUVRES

- **Charlie** was in several bands with his school mates before Busted (Recoil, Erase, Homesprung, Manhole and Spleen). One of the first was called Natural Disaster and they played in his school hall to raise money on Red Nose Day. Charlie was 11!
- **James** has worshipped Michael Jackson for as long as he can remember and reckons MJ was the first poster he ever put on his bedroom wall. He thanks the 'King Of Pop' for putting him where he is today. "I remember watching him on TV and wanting to be him. I definitely wouldn't be in Busted now if it wasn't for him."
- Unbelievable as it may seem, **James** spent the first five years of having guitar lessons thinking they were boring! Before he realised just how good he was at strumming those chords he confessed, "I just carried my guitar around 'cos I thought it looked cool!"
- **Matt** sang on a garage track called 'Sunshine' before he joined the band.

HEAD BOY
CAPTAIN
PREFEC

DUFFS
in the U.S.A.

Busted Buried... but where?

BUSTED

A	C	Y	O	U	S	A	I	D	N	O	R
B	J	B	D	F	A	R	E	E	F	A	Y
L	A	N	A	G	R	M	A	T	T	X	E
K	M	W	J	A	Q	V	M	I	U	I	U
O	E	E	P	N	M	R	U	S	L	T	B
P	S	Y	C	H	O	G	I	R	L	E	R
S	X	E	B	T	D	R	A	Q	O	N	I
T	G	B	L	M	T	H	Z	W	H	Y	T
F	E	R	K	S	C	H	O	O	L	T	N
L	T	O	H	B	S	P	I	Q	N	R	E
S	J	W	I	B	U	S	T	E	D	O	Y
M	I	S	S	M	C	K	E	N	Z	I	E

Try and uncover the tasty trio buried amongst the letters. There are eleven Busted related words to dig out... delve in!

BUSTED
CHARLIE
MATT
JAMES
GUITAR
MISS MCKENZIE
YOU SAID NO
EYEBROWS
BRITNEY
PSYCHO GIRL
SCHOOL

Busted Breakthrough

BUSTED

The Busted boys have broken through the charts with more speed than a souped up time machine. Here's how...

1999

- James and Mattie meet at a gig in Southend, where they talk all night about songwriting and decide to form a band.
- Matt moves into James's flat in Southend-on-sea and they start writing together.

2001

September

- The lads place an ad in music paper *NME* to find another guitarist.

October

- Charlie arrives at the audition with a guitar on his back and the boys think he looks too good to be true. James thinks, 'Please be able to play the guitar'. Matt thinks, 'Please be able to sing'. He can.
- One of Matt's mates is in a band called Buster. Matt's sister phones up *MTV Select* where Geri Halliwell is the guest host and asks to dedicate a song to them. Geri splutters, 'This one goes out to hot new band Busted!' Charlie, Matt and James decide to pinch the name for themselves. Busted is born.

2002

March

- After getting offers from record companies including Simon Cowell's label BMG, the boys sign on the dotted line with Universal Records.
- The three boys are moved into a swanky bachelor pad in Finchley, North London.

July

- Busted haven't even released a single yet - but are given a whole page in *Smash Hits* magazine who say they are "so impressed by Busted we had to make sure the pages of *Smash Hits* were where you saw them first".

August

- The rest of the pop press soon follows and it isn't long before the lads are the subjects of the prettiest posters in the land.

September

- Their debut single 'What I Go To School For' storms into the charts at number three.
- Their debut album *Busted* is released at the end of the month to rave reviews.

2003

January

- The boys bounce in at number two with their second single 'Year 3000'.

February

- The boys decide to change the name of their third single from 'Crash and Burn' to 'You Said No' out of respect for the crew of the Columbia who die in the space shuttle disaster.

March

- Busted's album goes platinum.
- Busted's big plan for world domination begins when they win two Bravo Supershow awards (the second biggest award show in Germany).

April

- Their third single 'You Said No' reaches number one! The boys celebrate by drawing a massive number one on James's back at the Spring Break Live concert.
- Charlie moves a few doors away from the flat to live with elder brother Will, although he says "I'm always popping round, just like in *Friends*".

May

- Busted begin their sell-out UK theatre tour.

August

- The lads release their fourth brilliant single 'Sleeping With The Lights On'.

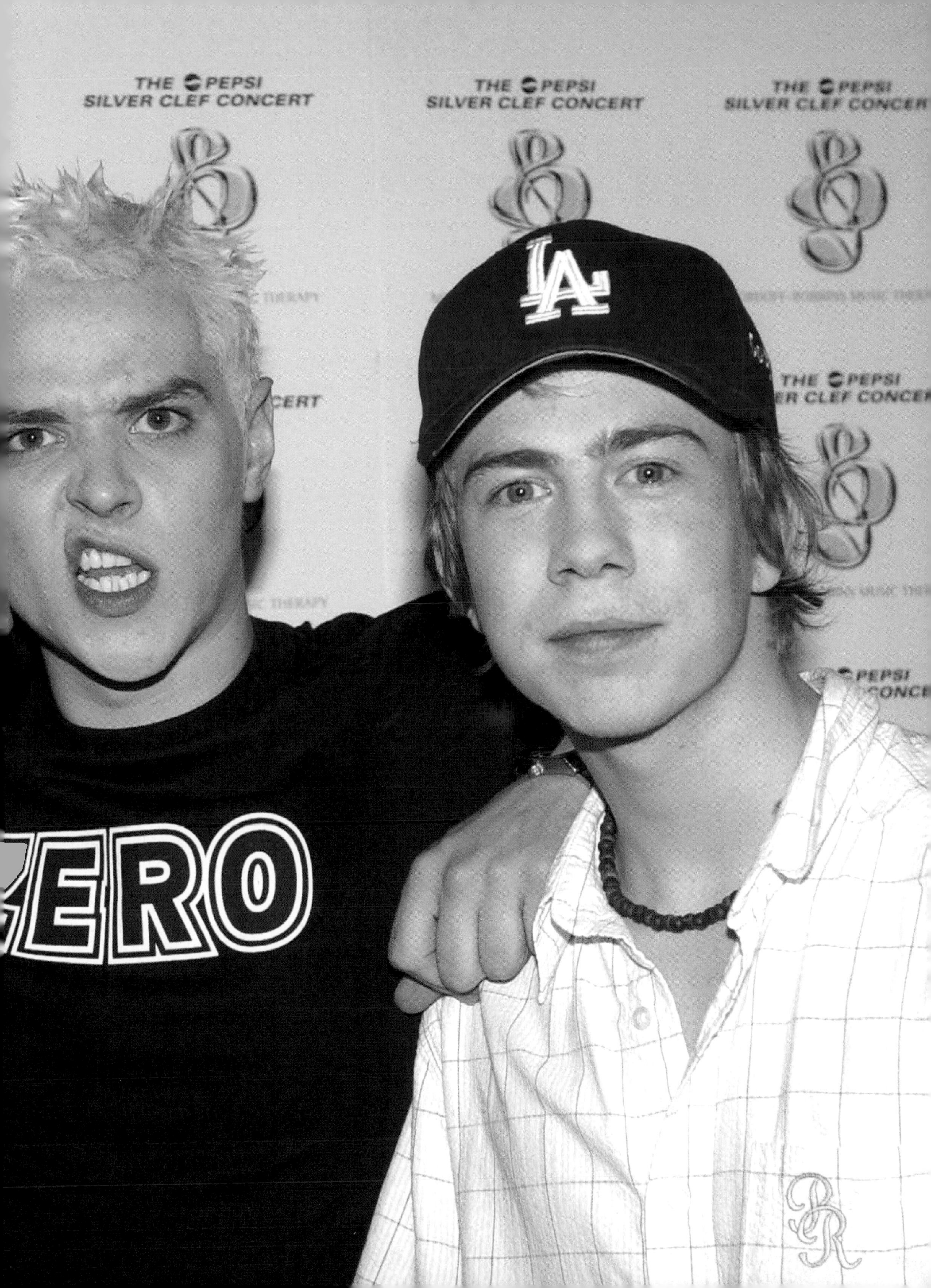
THE PEPSI
SILVER CLEF CONCERT
THE PEPSI
SILVER CLEF CONCERT
THE PEPSI
SILVER CLEF CONCER
LA
THE PEPSI
ER CLEF CONCER
CERT
ZERO

House Rules

When the cameras stop rolling and the guitars stop strumming it's time for the boys to go home, just like the rest of us. But what exactly is their home like? Who does the most washing up? Who's got the tidiest bedroom? Who makes the most mess? And more importantly - who spends the most time in the bathroom? You're about to find out...

FLAT FACTS

- The boys all live in the same apartment block in Finchley. **James** and **Matt** share one flat, which Charlie used to live in until he moved in with his brother Will (a few doors down). Matt laughs, "It's become much tidier and quieter since Charlie left!"
- **Matt** thinks their apartment is like a kids' palace: "It's got chandeliers and a big balcony. You walk into the dining room expecting to see a long table - and we've got a ping pong table instead!"
- The boys obviously don't think they do enough bouncing on stage because they've got their very own trampoline downstairs!
- **James**, **Matt** and **Charlie** love nothing more than watching TV on a huge screen while sitting in Joey-from-*Friends*-style armchairs.
- When **Charlie** was still living in the pad, the boys got loads of complaints from neighbours who said they were too noisy. It must've been Charlie's drum playing because Matt says, "They've stopped moaning now he's gone!"
- Girls Aloud live in apartment blocks right nearby (and for a while **Matt** was scared he'd bump into Nicola because he called her a rude name in a magazine interview. But he reckons they've sorted out their differences now).
- **Matt** makes sure he never gets locked out late at night - by cleverly keeping his keys attached to his belt chain.
- The boys have a cleaner who comes in each week to wash all their sheets.

BUSTED

BEDROOM BITS

- **Charlie** has a Bart Simpson lava lamp that his mum and dad bought him beside his bed.
- **James's** bedroom is really tidy because he says he doesn't spend much time in there unless he's asleep.
- **Charlie** doesn't make his bed because he reckons it's far more comfy to sleep in an unmade one – it's crinkly and cosy!
- When the lads first moved in together they drew straws for bedrooms. **James** got the best room with an en suite bathroom while **Charlie** got the smallest (no wonder he moved out!).
- All **Matt** has in his room is a CD player, a wardrobe and loads of guitars.
- **James** has done up his room so he's got shelves with all his bits on and pictures on the wall.
- **James** isn't much of a bedtime reader – he prefers to fall asleep watching his favourite films on DVD: "You can't beat *ET*, *Teenwolf* or *Back To The Future*," he says.
- When he's extra-tired **James** wears all his clothes to bed, but he usually sleeps in boxers and a T-shirt.
- **Matt** once dreamt that he was chatting to Samantha Mumba and all his front teeth fell out!

BUSTED

DOMESTIC DUDES?

- **Charlie** is the laziest lad of the group and would be the last one to ever put on rubber gloves and a pinny.
- **James** always leaves the lid off the toothpaste!
- **Matt** is the tidiest housemate by far – he's the only one in the band who knows how to use the washing machine and the dishwasher! (He's taught James how to use the dishwasher 13 times and he still can't do it!)
- **Charlie** used to leave cereal bowls everywhere – some even grew mould!
- **Matt** spends the most time in the bathroom (doing his hair).
- **Matt** once fell asleep in the lounge and when he woke at 5am and stepped off the sofa, he put his bare foot in a pizza that James had left on the floor (he wasn't impressed!).
- **Charlie** complains that James has "an amazing ability to make the toilet like a cess-pit". (It's a good job he has his own bathroom - eww!)
- **Matt** admits he's the biggest nag because he's always having to chase the other lads to tidy up after themselves.
- **Matt** makes a mean microwave lasagne.
- **Charlie's** speciality is a cheese and ham toastie.
- **Charlie** has never done his own washing.

BUSTED
DISNEY CHANNEL
KIDS AWARDS
AMONES
JOHNNY
TOMMY
JOEY

FLAMIN

Busted Confidential

BUSTED

They might be the raunchiest rule breakers on the planet – but our fave boys can still be a bit sentimental sometimes. There's a soft centre in each and every one of them...

TOP SECRET...

- **Charlie** is the soppiest soul in the band and loves watching slushy romantic movies like *What Women Want*, *Titantic* and *Dirty Dancing*. He's even got *The Princess Diaries* on video.
- **Matt** worries about his skin because he gets bad spots. 'They're the bane of my life,' he sobs.
- **James** tries to be tough when it comes to love, but he admits he's had a lot of heartache (he wrote 'Psycho Girl' about a girlfriend he just couldn't get out of his head).

MUSHY MATES

- **Matt** is great friends with Lee Ryan from Blue and says he couldn't have done without the support Lee gave him while they were waiting for their record deal. Bless.
- **Charlie**, **Matt** and **James** say they can't imagine life apart. Matt says, "It would be weird if I had to do this without them. I could never do this on my own."
- **Matt** makes sure he keeps in touch with all his mates back home because "they mean everything, don't they?"
- **Matt** carries old polaroids of Busted around with him in his wallet.
- **Charlie** took all his mates for a meal last time he was in Leicester. "I still miss them a lot," he says.
- **Matt** bought his best mates a sofa because they'd moved into a new place and didn't have anything to sit on.

BUSTED

FAMILY VALUES

- **James** has pictures of his family on his mantelpiece in the flat, so he can see their faces every day.
- **Matt** loves his little sister Amanda to death. He gushes, "She's such an inspiration to me – I tell her I love her all the time."
- **Charlie** can talk to his brothers about anything. Will's signed to a rock band which Charlie thinks is cool because "he's in the same industry".
- **Charlie** loves his bros so much he once bought them a guitar each ("they cost me an arm and a leg" he smiles).

STAR STRUCK

There are quite a few female stars that make the boys go weak at the knees, but there's also one male artist they are completely in awe of – Justin Timberlake! When James first met Justin he says, "I stood there thinking, 'Oh my god! It's Justin Timberlake!'" Matt adds, "I thought to myself 'You went out with Britney and Janet Jackson!'"
Charlie agrees, "I couldn't believe it when he spoke to us. He's one of the biggest stars in pop and he came up to us and said, 'Hi I'm Justin, I like your video'."
James nearly asked for Justin's number so they could hang out but he was worried he'd look like a stalker!

THE SENTIMENTAL THINGS

- **Charlie** used to have a teddy bear called Growler which he cuddled every night to help him get to sleep.
- **Charlie** still wears a ring that his ex-girlfriend Camilla gave him.
- **James** wears a necklace that Matt gave him before they got signed as a good luck charm.
- **Matt** still thinks about a girl he fancied when he was 14. He says, "Her name was Leanne and I fancied her so much it was unreal. I totally fell in love with her but she didn't fancy me back. But when I turned 16 I finally got her. I wish she'd get in touch and say hello."

Busted Crossword

Answers

Across
1. Posh
2. Back To The Future
3. Jim Carrey
4. Time Machine
5. Michael
6. Necklace
7. Taurus
8. Will

Down
8. West Ham
9. Smelly
10. Ed
11. Britney
12. Washing
13. No
14. Amanda
15. Cheese

Across

1. Another word for upper class (often used to describe Charlie) **(4)**
2. James's fave film starring Michael J Fox **(15)**
3. A rubbery faced actor James likes doing impersonations of **(9)**
4. A travelling device used in the video for 'Year 3000' **(11)**
5. The first name of James's high-voiced idol **(7)**
6. A good luck present Matt gave to James before they signed their record deal **(8)**
7. The star sign of the punkiest member of the band **(6)**
8. The name of a prince and Charlie's brother **(4)**

Down

8. Matt's fave footie team **(7)**
9. A word often used to describe Charlie's feet **(6)**
10. Name of Charlie's other brother (see 8 across) **(2)**
11. James and Charlie's ideal girl **(7)**
12. Clothes cleaning machine in the flat that only Matt knows how to use **(7)**
13. The word Busted's girl said when they asked her to dance at the disco (and last word of their third single) **(2)**
14. First name of Matt's sister **(6)**
15. A smelly food hated by Matt **(6)**

Live
13

Busted Babe Bible

BUSTED

With Charlie's traffic-stopping stare, James's 'cheeky chappy' smile and Mattie's mischievous grin, it's hardly surprising that these boys have babes begging to be their girlfriends. In this section you'll find out exactly what our Busted boys really look for in a lady, which famous fillies they've taken a fancy to, who's got the best chat-up technique and who'd take you on the dreamiest dates...

FAMOUS FANCIES

Matt

- Jennifer Love Hewitt: "She's got a sort of naughtiness and seems like she'd be a handful. I like that, it keeps me on my toes."
- Tara Reid (from *American Pie*): "She's just lovely!"

Charlie

- Britney Spears: "She sums up the best kind of woman there is – perfect looks, perfect hair, perfect body."
- Heidi Range: He denies they were ever an item but says the Sugababe is "one of the fittest girls in pop" and admits "I once sent her a text saying 'I like your bum!'"
- J.Lo: "We saw her at the *Maid In Manhattan* premiere and I wanted to grab her bottom!"
- Penelope Cruz: "She's so sophisticated."
- Sarah Whatmore: "She's looking really hot at the moment."

James

- Britney Spears (he's always arguing with Charlie about who loves her most): "She's divine."
- Jordana Brewster (from *The Faculty*): "She's got dark hair and she's fit."
- Holly Valance: "I'd love to kiss her – she's gorgeous!"

FAMOUS FIGHTS

There aren't many female folk who get on the wrong side of the lads, but when they do – they soon regret it!

Nicola Roberts from Girls Aloud once snubbed Matt at a celeb party. This was the start of a major feud between the two groups and resulted in Matt and Nicola both calling each other names in magazines. But being the forgiving type, Matt has decided to let Ms Roberts off the hook (and it's a good job too – because Girls Aloud have moved into the same apartment block as the Busted boys!).

Kelly Osbourne used to be the apple of Matt's eye (he told his mates that he thought she was "really pretty") – but, ever since she blanked them backstage at a TV concert, Matt has changed his tune. He insists, "I do not fancy Kelly-freakin-Osbourne – she's rough and pathetic." Nuff said!

DREAM DATES?

Charlie: "One Valentine's day I invited my girlfriend round and put rose petals in the bath, candles round the room and champagne on ice." He adds, "I like the idea of walking along the beach after a lovely meal in a posh restaurant."

Matt: "I'd take a girl for a kebab then go out clubbing – but then I'd grab her for a passionate snog on the dancefloor." Matt's dream date? "If I had my choice I'd take her to a rock concert. I wouldn't get her something cheesy like flowers, cos I hate soppiness."

James: "I'd pick a girl up in a DeLorean (flash car from *Back To The Future* movie), then I'd take her to a restaurant of her choice. I never forget to pick up the cheque after a date – because I'm a gentleman!"

DISASTROUS DATES

Charlie: "I was going out with a girl I really fancied and one night we stopped outside her house for a snog. I heard a noise and opened my eyes, only to see that she was staring at me while we were kissing! It really freaked me out and I ended up finishing with her the next day."

James: "When I was 12 I really fancied this girl at school, so a month before Valentine's day I made my own special card for her. I even painted a big heart on the front. But I forgot to put a stamp on the envelope when I posted it - so she never got it!"

Matt: "I tried to have a snogathon in a nightclub when I was 12. Me and my mate had a bet to see who could kiss the most girls. He snogged 34 and I got 16 – shocking isn't it?!"

CHAT UP TECHNIQUES

Who's got the most pulling power? Take a look at some of the boys' past passions and judge for yourselves…

James: "At our New Year's Eve party there was a girl crying in my bedroom. I walked in, picked up my guitar and started playing for her. She said she felt a lot better. That's how good I play!"

Charlie: "If I see a girl I like, I'll usually just ask her a question and start a conversation. I'll say something like 'Excuse me, do you know where the bar is? I'm Charlie by the way'. But I also like it when girls approach me."

Matt: "I try to make a girl smile. I broke the ice with a girl in a club by asking 'Excuse me, have you farted?' She couldn't stop laughing - it was genius!"

PERFECT PARTS

Here's what the lads have to say about their ideal girl…

Charlie: "I like conventional girls with a cool style that's really funky and fashionable. I used to think I went for blondes - until I saw *Vanilla Sky* and fancied Penelope Cruz. I like sophisticated and well-dressed girls. I don't go for tattoos or piercings on a girl."

Matt: "I tend to go for quite loud, upfront girls - but they end up turning into moody madams! I'm not really a dressy up kind of lad so I'm not impressed by anything too fancy."

James: "I like girls who are up for a laugh. Oh, and anyone who looks like Britney would suit me just fine!"

Which Busted Babe are you?

1.

Your Busted boy calls round to take you out, do you...

a) Head off to the most popular club in town and shake your stuff all night, before having a passionate snog on the dancefloor

b) Go for a romantic walk by the river, followed by a candlelit dinner at a posh restaurant

c) Go for a drive in a flashy sports car, then head home to watch *Back To The Future* on DVD while cuddling up to eat pizza

2.

You visit your boyfriend's house and have a peek in his bedroom, is it...

a) Empty except for some CDs and a pile of clean clothes on the bed

b) Full of DVDs with a picture of Michael Jackson hanging on the wall

c) Absolutely filthy - in fact, you can only just make out the drum kit that's hiding beneath the dirty clothes

3.

It's your boyfriend's birthday and you want to get him some clothes. What do you buy?

a) A smart black jacket – he looks great in classic clothes

b) A tight retro T-shirt – because he can't stand baggy tops

c) Anything bright – he's a skater boy at heart

4.

You ask your boyfriend to express how much he loves you, does he...

a) Write you a romantic slushy poem then sprinkle rose petals around your bedroom

b) Tell you he loves you because your bum's so big and beautiful

c) Put on his best Jim Carrey impression and moonwalk across the room while singing "I love you yeah yeah yeah"

5.

You meet your boy's friends for the first time, do they say...

a) 'Hi, I'm Prince William, I'm a good friend of your chap's family'

b) 'Alright darlin', howz it hangin? When are you coming to the West Ham match with us?'

c) 'Woo – who! We're bad! We're off to visit Never Land – you coming?"

6.

You want to change your hairstyle, what does he say?

a) 'You should grow it long. I love simple, pretty styles'

b) 'Yeah! Go for it! Why don't you have it all chopped off and dye it red?'

c) 'I don't mind how you have it. Although Britney's hair is looking nice at the moment'

7.

You think your Busted boy looks perfect, but he thinks...

a) 'I'm so spotty it really gets me down sometimes'

b) 'My farts are sooo loud!'

c) 'I wish my feet would stop smelling!'

Answers:

1. a) 1 b) 2 c) 3
2. a) 1 b) 3 c) 2
3. a) 2 b) 1 c) 3
4. a) 2 b) 1 c) 3
5. a) 2 b) 1 c) 3
6. a) 2 b) 1 c) 3
7. a)1 b) 3 c) 2

Mostly 1's: Make magic with Matt

There's no denying that your ideal date is wild child Matt. You love a laugh and aren't afraid to express your personality by standing out from the crowd. You want someone who's up for a good time and will whisk you off your feet – even if it means nipping off for a kebab afterwards!

Mostly 2's: Charlie's your angel

Smiles and silliness are all very well, but when it comes to lads you want a pair of gorgeous cheekbones to stare at while you're being treated to a romantic meal. You're not afraid of showing your serious side, and you'll happily hang with his posh friends if it means getting a gentle kiss afterwards.

Mostly 3's: Juicy James is the one for you

You like your boy to be cute and a big kid at heart. You love watching films and your favourite movie star is Jim Carrey because he's so funny. Dancing round the room to Michael Jackson tunes ranks high on your things-to-do list!

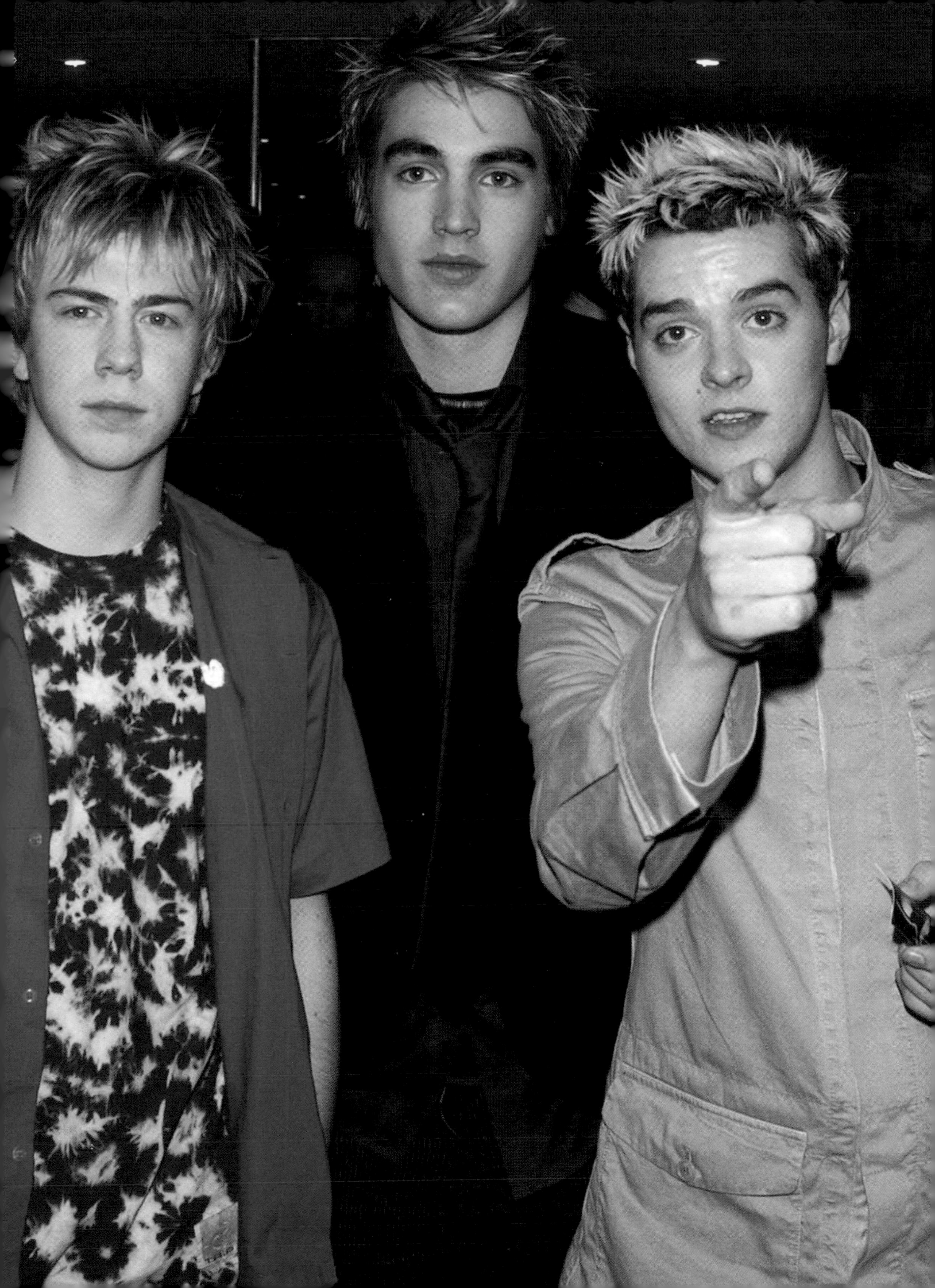

Which Busted Boy are you?

BUSTED

1.
You invite your mates over for the afternoon, do you...
a) Play footie in the garden
b) Watch the Prince William documentary
c) Watch *Back To The Future* on DVD ✓

2.
There's a girl in the corner of the room at a party. You fancy her like mad - what does she look like?
a) Tall, classically beautiful with long blonde hair
b) Avril Lavigne
c) Pink hair and the loudest outfit in the room

3.
You need some new threads, do you buy...
a) A retro T-shirt and baggy trousers (with your pants sticking out)
b) A jacket and tie
c) A surfer shirt and long shorts

4.
What is your worst habit?
a) Burping
b) Smelly feet
c) Stinking the toilet out

5.
When it comes to housework you think...
a) "I'll tidy my bedroom but the rest of the house can look after itself"
b) "Housework? What's that?"
c) "It has to be done. I hate a messy house"

6.
People laugh at you because...
a) You're always doing impressions of famous people
b) You're cheeky and rude
c) You like to add your own endings to words

7.
You've got a music voucher. What do you spend it on?
a) The alternative stuff
b) Punk and hip hop
c) Pop - of course!

Answers:
1. a) 1 b) 2 c) 3
2. a) 2 b) 3 c) 1
3. a) 1 b) 2 c) 3
4. a) 1 b) 2 c) 3
5. a) 3 b) 2 c) 1
6. a) 3 b) 1 c) 2
7. a) 2 b) 1 c) 3

Mostly 1's: Mad like Matt
You're quite the unique individual. You've got a cheeky sense of fun and have a big group of mates who all mean a lot to you. Not one to follow the rules, you'd much rather spend your time hanging with a girl who's outgoing and loud than having a pretty wallflower on your arm. But your wild ways don't mean you're a slob – if you make a mess you always clean up afterwards!

Mostly 2's: A Chap like Charlie
Just like Busted's poshest resident, you are a lad who enjoys the finer things in life. You have your own special sense of humour and your upper class ways always make your mates laugh (without you even realising sometimes!). When it comes to the ladies, you're very fussy – you like your girl to be traditionally feminine and pretty and like to play the gentleman whenever you're with her. But being posh doesn't mean you're boring – you're passionate about music and love nothing more than moshing the night away at an indie music gig.

Mostly 3's: Just like James
Forget going out – your idea of a good time is stuffing your face with pizza and watching DVDs of your fave films from the eighties. You and your mates can spend hours reciting lines from movies like *Back To The Future* and *The Mask* and you have them all in stitches with your brilliant impersonations. On the girl front, you're holding out for that special lady, but when she finally arrives you'll shower her with affection.

Style Secrets

BUSTED

These lads are a cut above the rest when it comes to clothes. With their funky punk threads and multi-coloured manes, Busted manage to be edgy, grungy, smart and sexy all at the same time. This section gives you everything you need to know about their look...

MATT

"the punky one"

Matt's style has evolved a lot since the band first began. He's moved from dressing like a cross between Sid Vicious and Dennis the Menace to looking cooler and more classically rock, taking his inspiration from bands like the Foo Fighters and Nirvana. Matt's not afraid of trying out new stuff (he once wore black eyeliner on *CD:UK*) but he likes his hair to do most of the talking and prefers his clothes to be dark in colour. He loves retro, tight-fitting T-shirts from vintage markets like Portobello or Camden (don't try to put him in a big top – he'll think it's a duvet cover). Matt's trousers are notoriously baggy (he's not afraid of letting his pants show!) and anything denim is a winner with him. On Mr Jay's feet you'll always see old skool trainers – nothing too shiny and new for this chappie.

JAMES

"the skater boy"

James's style sits in the middle of Matt and Charlie's. He's a big fan of customised clothes (Busted's stylist often adds a few go-faster stripes on his shirts or trousers to make them stand out from the norm). James loves anything from skater/surfer shops like Mambo or Stussy and will usually wear a bright shirt over a long-sleeved T-shirt. Down below he likes to dress in baggy long shorts – but these are usually bought as trousers, then cut down afterwards (he says long shorts bought straight from the shop don't fit as nicely). James loves baggy T-shirts and can't get enough of strong logos like the Skull and Crossbones or The Incredible Hulk. Petrol blue is a favourite colour of his. As for shoes: the bigger the better as far as James is concerned (even if he looks like he's wearing two loaves of bread on his feet!). He loves brands like Vans and Etnies. He always wears the beaded necklace that Matt gave him.

BUSTED

CHARLIE

"posh boy"

Charlie's look manages to combine designer threads with skater kid (a bit like a surfer boy who's gone to Eton!). Charlie enjoys wearing smart tailored jackets that have been scruffed up with 1950s retro patches (like logos from old companies that don't exist any more). His jackets are normally black and single breasted and he teams them with ties (he wore a black and white checked tie on the Busted tour); then underneath he likes to wear bright T-shirts. Charlie's long legs are often covered in baggy cords or big skater pants. He is happy to wear old skool trainers like Matt or chunky footwear like James. Charlie's fave things are burgundy T-shirts and his chocolate brown tie. He likes dressing for the occasion!

DARE TO WEAR

- Matt once forgot that one of his T-shirts had a red symbol on the back of it - and when he shoved it in the washing machine it turned everything else pink!
- Charlie says he'd be most embarrassed if a girl saw his socks – because "sometimes I wear the same ones twice!"
- Matt once got a job in high street clothes shop Next, but when he found out he had to wear a smart shirt and trousers to work he walked out!
- Matt says he nicked his hairstyle from a bass player in old indie rock band The Dum Dums (his mum hates it though!).
- Matt's most embarrassing outfit is a long-sleeved top with a denim patch and an 'N' in sequins on it. It cost him £50!!

TROUSER TALK

Fortunately for Matt's fans his trousers have a funny habit of falling down whenever he's on stage! He reckons it's because he never does his belt up tight enough – but he insists he always wears pants underneath (shame!).

Busted Behaving Badly

BUSTED

They fancy their teacher, they thrash around the stage like a trio of pukka punks and they've got more cheek than J.Lo's bum. So it's hardly surprising that Matt, James and Charlie like to get a bit naughty in their spare time...

PRACTICAL JOKERS

- **Charlie** hates the band Nickelback, so cheeky **James** and **Matt** once put a request on the website for fans to send him as much Nickelback stuff as they could!
- **James** and **Matt** always take the mickey out of **Charlie's** posh voice but Charlie shrugs, "I just smile and take the abuse."
- At a TV gig, the lads decided to play a trick on fellow popster Daniel Bedingfield. They followed him into a portaloo and started singing his song while he was having a wee until he shouted 'Who's that singing my song?'!
- **James** once pretended there was a massive spider on **Charlie's** back (Charlie hates spiders!) and **Charlie** jumped so high he nearly flew through the ceiling.
- When they were on a plane once James ate his pudding really fast just to make **Matt** laugh.
- **Matt** and **James** annoy **Charlie** by singing songs by The Streets – but putting in their own words like "Lady bring two full English over with plenty of scrambled egg".
- **Charlie** also gets annoyed when Mattie puts on his silly opera voice and sings 'Year 3000'!
- When they're on a plane and there's turbulence **James** likes to stare at **Charlie** in a funny way to make him nervous.

BANNED BOYS

Busted got banned from a hotel in Germany after partying all night with Lee from Blue. They had to beg to be let back in - then the boys overslept the next morning, missed their flight and Charlie was sick in Mattie's suitcase!

BUFF OR GUFF?

They might look pretty, but these boys aren't at all shy when it comes to discussing the smellier things in life…

- **James:** "If I'm going to fart I get someone to pull my finger so at least they get a warning!"
- **Matt** reckons Charlie once stunk the car out with a really smelly fart!
- **James** once thought a slug was a wine gum and tasted it!
- **James** wees in the shower (and swimming pools).
- **Charlie** once weed in a park next to the millennium wheel!
- **James** loves the smell of his own farts and used to play a game called the Dutch Oven (where he'd fart and pull the covers over his head!).

Behind the Videos

'What I Go To School For'
Release date 16 September 2002
Chart position 3

- The song is based on a true story about Matt's crush on his science teacher.
- The school used for the classroom scenes is a disused school in Middlesex. Charlie says he found it creepy walking down the corridors with all the empty classrooms…
- It took three days to film.
- The stuntman who taught Matt to fall from a tree used to work on James Bond movies!
- The boys had a lot of hanging around but luckily there was a pool table for them to play on in between takes.
- The lads had originally asked their mates to be in the video too - but Charlie says "as soon as the 5.30am start was mentioned they weren't interested!"
- The production team had to go shopping for 200 school ties for the extras in the video.
- Matt had to fall out of the tree 15 times!
- The Bacardi Breezer cat was hired to play Miss McKenzie's cat, but it was sick so they had to hire a replacement.
- Charlie had to wait under a blanket for three hours for the rain to stop, before he could shoot his fantasy scene where he is running through a field after Miss McKenzie in his underwear.
- James has become an expert at moonwalking – but unfortunately the Doc Martens he wore left him with blisters all over his feet.
- The boys thought they were going to be driving off into the sunset with Miss McKenzie in a convertible Porsche – and were very disappointed when a Vauxhall Cavalier turned up!
- Matt couldn't sit down for two days after filming his fantasy scene with Miss M – because she spanked him so hard!

'Year 3000'
Release date 20 January 2003
Chart position 2

- James's younger brother Chris was in the video as the inventor of the time machine.
- Matt nearly ended up pant-less during the vid because 150 fans went crazy for the lads! "I couldn't believe it when all these girls started grabbing my bits!" said Mattie. (But the crafty cutie must've enjoyed the scene - because he did it 12 times!)
- Matt's older double in the video was a wizard in the Harry Potter films!
- The video cost a whopping £130,000 to make!
- There are loads of references to *Back To The Future* in the vid (it's James's fave film and was the inspiration for the song).
- Busted's stylist Mr Gammon embroidered the lyrics to the song on the guys' clothes.

'You Said No'
Release date 21 April 2003
Chart position 1

- The sexy nurse who helps James when he falls over was supposed to be a model, but she pulled out at the last minute – so they picked the prettiest fan in the audience to play her instead!
- During the scene when Busted have to flirt with their love interests they deliberately kept getting bits wrong so they had to keep re-shooting the section. What a tough job!
- James's fave part of the vid is the shot when the shadow falls around them while they're performing in the skate pipe.
- There was a real cat fight at one point between two groups of fans who came down to watch the video being filmed, but Matt saved the day and stepped in saying "What's going on? Break it up!"
- They put an ad on their website for fans to come down to the shoot and were shocked by the response. James said, "We only expected 150 to turn up but 400 showed!"
- In the video the boys' names appear as Charlie 'Psycho' Simpson, Matt 'Mad Dog' Jay and James 'Chopper' Harris (even though his real surname is Bourne). This was due to a bit of tomfoolery between James and the video director. In an on-set game of football, James tackled someone in the style of the legendary Chelsea footballer Ron 'Chopper' Harris. The director decided to change James's name for a joke, but forgot to put it back before it went on TV.

'Sleeping With The Lights On'
Release date 11 August 2003

- This video is a departure from the band's previous stuff – and was shot in slow motion so the boys look a bit more edgy and grown-up than before. The idea behind the video is that all the boys fall in love with the same girl.
- The model who played their love interest was called Rebecca (and they all fancied her!).
- Fans from all over the country came to play extras in the video – and some of them were so dedicated that they stayed right until the end of filming at 11.30pm. The boys were concerned that they were OK and kept coming to check on them and give them food to eat.
- Matt wanted to get a coke to drink but felt really bad when someone from the crew got one for him, because he felt he should have gone to the shop himself!
- The shoot took two days and was filmed in London. It was meant to be top secret but one of the scenes coincidentally took place next door to an all-girls school (unsurprisingly, the boys had a fair few admirers when school was out at 3.30!!).

BUSTED

Did you know?

- **James** still tries to catch the underground from home and hides his blond locks under a cap.
- If either **Matt** or **Charlie** left Busted, **James** would replace them with Avril Lavigne.
- If **James** could have any job in the world other than being in Busted, he'd be the person who does Bart Simpson's voice so he could say 'I'm Bart Simpson'.
- **Matt's** mum regularly calls him up and says 'Are you ever going to pull a nice face?'
- **Matt** says: "When Charlie records his vocals in the studio he always stands in a beanie hat with his arm going up and down. He turns into some kind of rapper! It comes out of nowhere 'cos he's the poshest guy I've ever met in my life and suddenly he turns into Eminem!"
- **Matt** hates being called Mattie.
- **Charlie's** brother Ed goes to St Andrews University and plays rugby with Prince William – his dad has even got a picture of him on the wall!
- **James's** all time fave record is 'Bohemian Rhapsody' by Queen.
- **Matt** won the 'Best Performance Like A Fish Award' in *Smash Hits* 2003.
- **Charlie's** great granddad was a composer.
- **Busted** are massive in Germany – in 2003 they beat major rockers Bon Jovi and Linkin Park to win the best rock gong at German pop magazine *Bravo*'s Supershow Awards ceremony.
- **Busted** recorded an exclusive single for their German fans (and they decided to sing it in German as a way to say thank you - or *danke*!).

Zildjian

Psychic James's Future Predictions

James might be a clever chap but he reckons his powers go beyond the brain! He is convinced he's got psychic abilities and can tell what's going to happen in the future. He says, "I get premonitions. I once dreamt that Michael Jackson was standing at a bus stop on Oxford Street wearing a black jacket. Three days later I saw him on TV wearing the same jacket I'd dreamt about."
Spooky stuff! We decided to show you what Mr Bourne would see for Busted if he had his own crystal ball...

Planet James
Star sign: Virgo
Characteristics:
(Good) Modest, reliable, hardworking, intelligent, careful with money.
(Bad) Fussy, a worrier, overcritical, perfectionist.
Predictions: There's a very good year ahead for James, but he must be careful not to become over confident. Busted will continue to grow in popularity and James's life will be full of changes for the better (there'll be plenty of travel, new places to visit and even more fans). James shouldn't be surprised if he gets given extra responsibility at work (perhaps he'll start learning how to produce Busted's songs?). It'll be a great year for making things come true and asking for favours – so maybe it's time to ask the record company to buy him that DeLorean sports car he's always wanted. James will look and feel great this year as he starts to accept just how gorgeous he really is. There's a possibility he might buy a home for someone in his family. As far as romance goes, James is unlikely to find the love of his life this year (he is a perfectionist after all) but one thing's for sure – he'll have lots of fun trying!

Planet Charlie
Star sign: Gemini
Characteristics:
(Good) Adaptable, witty, communicative, lively, eloquent.
(Bad) Nervous, inconsistent, cunning, critical, bad with money, easily bored.
Predictions: Charlie's year will have him in a flirty and fancy-free mood as he swaps numbers with even more lucky ladies at celebrity parties. But heaven help any girl trying to catch him – she'll need to get her blades on if she wants to keep up with him! Charlie's relationships will be light-hearted rather than heavy-going (it's possible he'll go out with someone younger than him for a while and he might also start to fancy more unusual girls than his normal type). Charlie needs to be careful while he's painting the town all the colours of the rainbow though – because his health could suffer a bit (he may end up in bed with exhaustion). Still, his popularity will continue to soar sky high and he certainly won't be complaining!

Planet Matt
Star sign: Taurus
Characteristics:
(Good) Patient, reliable, warm-hearted, security-loving, kind.
(Bad) Jealous, stubborn, cautious, possessive.
Predictions: This year Matt will be able to enjoy some of the money he's earned – it's taken him a while to realise that all that money in his bank account really does belong to him, but at last he'll feel free to spend spend spend! Busted will be doing a lot of travelling this year and it's likely that Matt will meet someone new who'll give him some very useful tips for the future (maybe he'll learn a few skateboard tricks at least!). Like the rest of the band, he won't be short of admirers, and Matt is likely to find he's attracted to people who come from very different backgrounds (maybe he'll fancy a girl from another country?). This year Matt stands a very good chance of falling in love because, for once, he's not looking for it.

The year 2003 was a mental year for the boys. Aside from partying, mingling with fellow celebs and trying to dodge hordes of admiring fans, they've been pogo hopping their way into our cities and into our hearts, with their first sell-out UK tour.

FANS

- James admits: "We all have our own circles of fans. I get a lot of quiet girls and the mums. Matt gets the louder girls. But Charlie gets the beautiful fans. Charlie's female following has gone stratospheric on this tour."
- Charlie says: "We got some rude banners. If I saw one I'd always point it out to the other two. Once I was playing and I noticed a girl had pulled her top up and had my name written on her chest!"
- Everton's fabulous footballer Wayne Rooney is one of their biggest fans and was a guest of honour at one of their gigs.

ON STAGE

- Busted were joined by a band on stage so their gigs were 100% live!
- Matt's fans always got a cheeky treat when they saw him in concert because of his recurring habit of dropping his trousers on stage! Matt says, "I once enjoyed the screams so much that when they died away, I had to show my bum so I could hear them again!"
- Busted's shows weren't like any ordinary pop concert - oh no. Charlie says: "There's no cheesiness! It's just a really good rock-orientated show. There isn't any silly pop stuff like flying through the sky. I've got no time for that."
- At one of their gigs, during a part of the song where he didn't have to play, Matt put his guitar on his back and climbed on top of a massive speaker – but didn't realise quite how high it was until he got there!
- Matt once got the urge to stage dive during a performance of 'Year 3000', but as he leapt he got his legs caught in his guitar strap and fell into a little ball! The next day he woke up with a broken toe.

BACKSTAGE

- The band arrived at each venue around 4ish, when they'd have a snack and a soundcheck. Dinner would be eaten at six (so they weren't playing on a full stomach), then Matt, James and Charlie would either hang in their dressing room or go back to their hotel to get ready for the show.

- The crew had a crew room near the band's dressing room and the lads would often pass the time chatting to the crew and swapping (dirty!) jokes.
- A whopping ten miles of cable was used to wire up the equipment at each Busted gig!
- After each gig the band would go back to their hotel bar to mingle with fans and chat about the show. Meanwhile, the crew would shower on the tour bus and pack up the equipment until about 1am!
- While they were doing their soundchecks Matt wore his special rehearsal pants because he said: "I get too sweaty if I rehearse in jeans."
- Busted travelled on Oasis's tour bus – which was very rock'n'roll (although James was worried they'd find Liam Gallagher's teeth on the floor! Eww!).
- James says he'd never have survived without his phone on the road because it kept him sane.
- Charlie always brought a pillow on long journeys – he couldn't sleep on the bus without one.
- Matt once got annoyed because he forgot his hair gel at a gig – but he says, "I was only annoyed with myself."

TOUR DATES

- The lads toured the UK between May and June 2003, appearing in cities across the country.
- Charlie's fave gig was the Manchester Apollo, because when he and his mates went there to watch Korn a few years ago, they told him "We're going to see you on that stage one day!"
- Matt loved touring in London because that's where most of his family were watching from the wings.

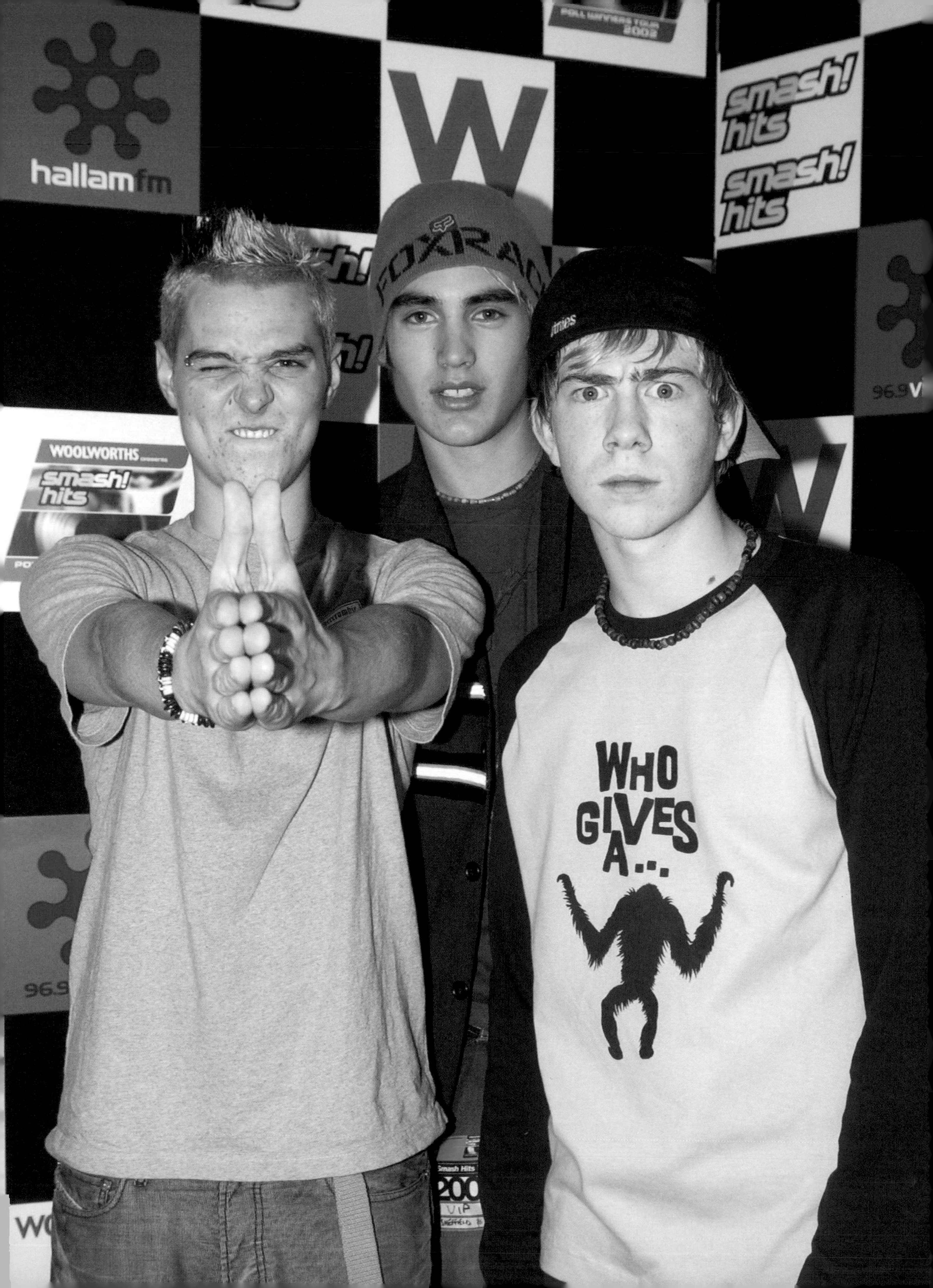

POLL WINNERS TOUR 2002
hallamfm
smash! hits
smash! hits
WOOLWORTHS
smash! hits
WHO GIVES A...
Smash Hits

Busted's Bigger Things To Come

BUSTED

Following the success of their sold-out theatre concerts, the lads have announced an arena tour starting in March 2004 - showing just how big the band has grown over the last few months (arenas seat up to 12,000 people – so imagine how loud those screams are going to be!).
James hopes his dreams of being able to duet with Michael Jackson or Justin Timberlake will become a reality this year, and now that Mr Timberlake has told them he liked their video for 'You Said No' - who knows what could happen?

The lads are nearly finished writing their second album, which they promise will be "the best second album ever". James says at least one of the songs is about all the pesky girls who've made up stories about the band (pretending they've snogged them when they haven't! Tut!).
Unlike most bands, Busted have written all their songs, which means this year they'll see their royalties (hard earned cash) flooding into their bank accounts – so expect to see Matt, James and Charlie flashing a fair bit of cash (Porsches, castles, you name it!).

With plenty of trips abroad and promotional visits to other countries, the boys look set for world domination! And one thing's for certain: The Busted bubble is about to get bigger and bigger...

BUSTED

Discography

WHAT I GO TO SCHOOL FOR

A cheeky tribute to Matt's old science teacher (although in real life Matt didn't actually end up going out with his teach!).

James: "When I look back on this album this'll end up being my favourite song. It'll always be the song that introduced Busted to the world."

YOU SAID NO

A rabble-rousing tale of rejection in front of your mates.

Matt: "We were absolute losers at school. I remember the first time I was blown out, I felt like such an idiot!"

BRITNEY

An touching display of affection towards a certain Ms Spears.

Fascinating fact: a line about Britney's ex Mr Timberlake - 'Throw Justin in the bin' - was removed from the final cut because the boys are such huge fans of his.

LOSING YOU

Charlie thinks this ballad is the cheesiest song on the album. But Matt argues, "It's high quality cheese – it's brie not Tesco Value cheddar!"

YEAR 3000

Influenced by James's fave film *Back To The Future*.

Matt says: "The chorus is a bit of a lyrical fiasco because if it's in 998 years it'd be more than your "great, great, great granddaughter". But the correct number of 'greats' wouldn't fit!"

PSYCHO GIRL

One of James's fave songs on the album – written about a girl he knows. He says: "We didn't agree on anything and I couldn't stand being with her but at the same time I really needed her. I always end up with psycho girls!"

ALL THE WAY

Matt explains: "It's about girls that tease you. Girls who lead you on…"

SLEEPING WITH THE LIGHTS ON

This is the first song that James and Matt ever wrote together so it's very special. All the boys agree that the line "Sharks swim through my veins" is the most emotional lyric on the album.

DAWSONS GEEK

Originally called 'Vain Boy', this song was written about a kid they knew. James realised the kid looked like James Van Der Beek who plays Dawson in the TV show *Dawson's Creek* - so they changed the title. "This song was done in seven minutes," announces James proudly!

WHEN DAY TURNS INTO NIGHT

A moody, low-key song about being away from home (written when they were staying in hotels looking for record deals).

Matt and Charlie both say it's among their favourites on the album.

EVERYTHING I KNEW

Although it sounds like a happy, anthemic, bouncy Busted tune – this is actually another song about a broken relationship. "It's about thinking 'why did I let her go?'" says Charlie.

WITHOUT YOU

A song written by Charlie a couple of years ago, when he was going out with a girl two years above him at school. "All her friends were telling her to stop going out with me," he says, "But age shouldn't matter in relationships." (We bet she's gutted now!)

LOSER KID

This song is set a year on from 'What I Go To School For' – and the boys are living with Miss Mckenzie at this stage… so they're not loser kids any more!!

Bust or Sussed?

BUSTED

So you think you're Busted's biggest fan? Time to find out...

1. What is Matt's fave CD?
2. What did Charlie do to upset the neighbours when he was living with James and Matt?
3. Who keeps photos of his family on his mantelpiece, so he can see them every day?
4. List Busted's first three singles and what position they reached in the charts.
5. Which former Spice Girl was responsible for their name?
6. Who once put chewing gum behind their ear?
7. What does Charlie's mum call him?
8. Who is the sportiest member of the band?
9. What does Matt hate being called?
10. What is the name of Busted's stylist?
11. What is James's fave film?
12. What is Matt's speciality in the kitchen?
13. Which girl popster did Matt have a feud with?
14. Who has a Simpsons lava lamp by their bed?
15. How many seconds can Matt burp for?
16. What is the name of Charlie's old teddy bear?
17. Who does Matt think Charlie looks like when he sings in the studio?

Answers

1. *Make Yourself* by Incubus
2. Played his drums too loudly
3. James
4. 'What I Go To School For' – 3, 'Year 3000' – 2, 'You Said No' – 1
5. Geri Halliwell
6. Matt
7. Farley or Farleykins
8. James
9. Mattie
10. Mr Gammon
11. *Back To The Future*
12. Microwave lasagne
13. Nicola from Girls Aloud
14. Charlie
15. 26
16. Growler
17. Eminem